Scout's Honor

For all our little Pinocchios.

May this book help you find your Jiminy Cricket!

ISBN: 978-1-7355225-5-5
LCCN: 2021918682

Oops!

"This cannot be good,"

says Scout.

Scout wonders,
"What do I do? Do I tell a lie or the truth?"

"It could be fun to tell mom a story about how the wind blew the lamp over!"
Scout giggled to himself.

Scout remembers that the window is closed.
"Then again, mom will know that I lied. She may never trust me again."

"Oh! I know! I can clean up the lamp quick and no one will know!"

"But I will know and keeping the secret will make me worried sick."

Scout thinks some more.
"If I tell the truth, there will be
trouble for sure."

"But if I tell a lie, I will be in double trouble and that is way worse!"

"So, I think I will tell the truth!"

"The truth will make me feel good!"

"Telling the truth will make my mom and dad proud of me!"

"And I will be a leader of doing what is right even when it is scary."

"Mom! Dad! I have something to tell you!"

Scout shouts as he bravely skips away to tell the truth!

Hi readers!

Thanks for reading Scout's Honor. As a children's book author, I typically write fun rhyming books that introduce young kids to possible careers and empower their present and their future. But when my five-year-old went from being a truthteller to a storyteller, I knew I had to nip it and there's no better way than with a good book. So, I hope Scout's Honor was not only an enjoyable read, but a helpful read to you and yours!

Tiffany Obeng

www.SugarCookieBooks.com
SugarCookieBooks@gmail.com
@SugarCookieBooks

If you enjoyed Scout's Honor, please leave an honest five-star rating and review on Amazon.com so other young readers can find this book.

OTHER BOOKS BY TIFFANY OBENG

Career Books for Kids
Andrew Learns about Actors
Andrew Learns about Teachers
Andrew Learns about Lawyers
Andrew Learns about Engineers

Seasons Books for Kids
Winnie Loves Winter
Spencer Knows Spring
Fallon Favors Fall
Sutton's Summer Vibes

SEL Books for Kids
My Summer Skin is Radiant
The Night The Lights Went Out
Two Houses Down: A Story for Children about
Divorce and Friendship

Spanish Books for Kids
Andrew aprende sobre los actores
I Have 10 Toes / Tengo Diez Dedos De Los Pies

More Books for Kids
I Have 10 Toes, Thank You Jesus
Animals in the Forest Coloring & Activity Book

Made in the USA
Columbia, SC
07 October 2022